Pat and Tam

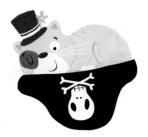

Written by
Jill Atkins

Illustrated by
Angelika Scudamore

Ransom

Pat has a fat cat, Tam.

Tam is a fat cat in a hat.

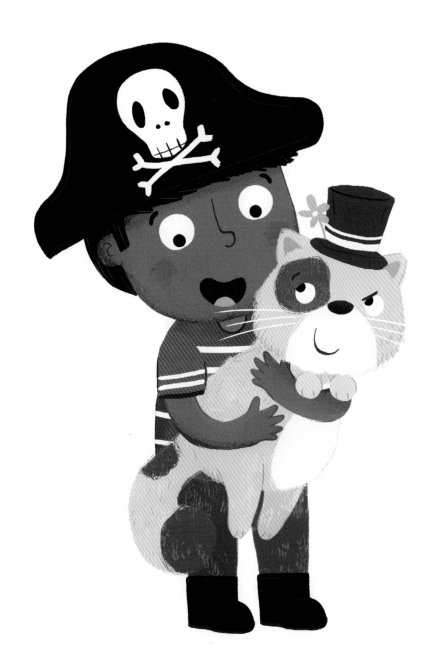

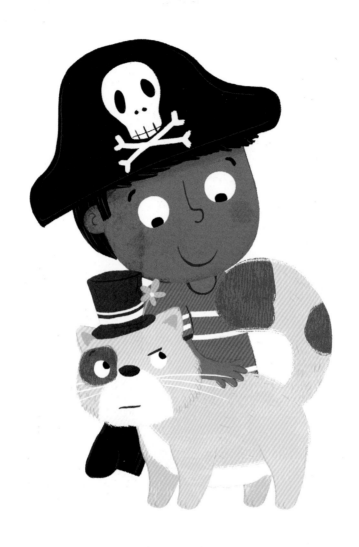

Pat can pat Tam.

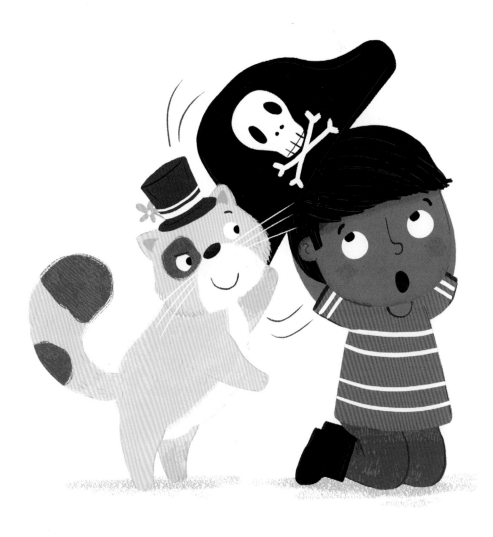

Tam can tap Pat.

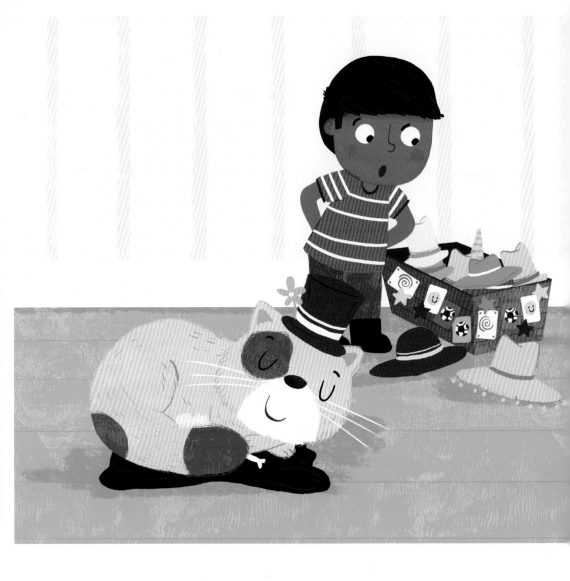

Pat has no hat.

Can Pat get a hat?

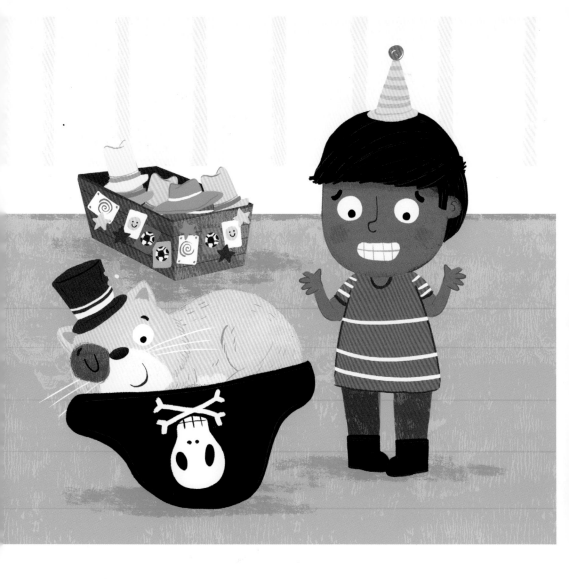

Pat has a hat.

But it is a bad hat.

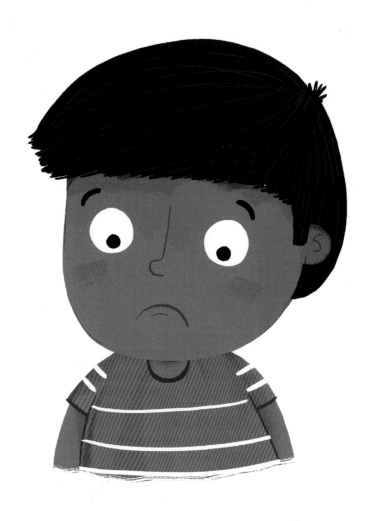

Is Pat sad?